42 Delicious Fat-Burning Recipes

What Others Have To Say About
Advantage Personal Training LLC.

Awesome gym with the best trainers and staff in the area. Professional, CLEAN, and fun! They have built an encouraging and supportive community that really sets them apart from any other gym. *- Joanna M*

What a great place to workout and decompress!! The trainers are all knowledgeable and awesome. Their staff there is just second to none. I highly recommend APT. *- Mel N*

I love the APT family... that is what you become when you join this great place! Friendly, encouraging, motivating, knowledgeable trainers, great environment and don't forget the yummy shakes. They work with you to personalize every workout to what YOU need to meet your goal/s - today, tomorrow, and longer-term. Thanks to APT I am stronger and healthier every day. *- Carrie R*

THIS IS THE PLACE TO BE!! (Especially if you hate the typical "gym" mentality!) The trainers are great people who know their STUFF!! You will work hard, you will be pushed, you will be supported, you will be motivated, you can do your own thing, you can ask for help, you will make new friends, you will be part of a community...the list goes on... *- Sherri B*

Contents

Real Healthy Entrees

Introduction

I'm going to show you how you can eat great tasting food and still lose weight and look great. Is your diet healthy and nutritious? If you're serious about being in great shape, then you know how important it is to eat "clean". What's clean eating? Eating clean is just another way of saying eating foods that will help you achieve your most wanted goals.... For most people those goals are losing fat, not feeling deprived, having more energy and looking tone and tight. Cooking healthy meals at home is the best way to ensure that the food you eat is prepared with high quality ingredients and with the healthiest cooking methods. In this cookbook you will find 42 recipes that will encourage your fitness results, while still tasting delicious. You may notice the term real healthy throughout the following pages, so let me clarify what that means... In order to be truly healthy a food item must be real. Real foods include organic meat, poultry, eggs, vegetables, fruits, nuts and seeds. These real foods are ideal fuel for your body and will encourage your body to burn off excess fat storage. So put down the processed, packaged and genetically modified convenience food and instead make a recipe with real, wholesome ingredients. Your taste buds and your skinny jeans will both be happy! Real Healthy Breakfast: Donuts, muffins and pancakes? How can I call these recipes healthy? It's all in the ingredient substitutions. Rather than wheat flour you'll use coconut or almond flour. These real food flours bring the carb count of the recipe much lower than traditionally made donuts, muffins and pancakes. There is also more protein and fat in these real food flours, which will fuel your day and keep you going without the mid-morning energy crash. Real Healthy Snacks: Most popular snack foods come from shiny plastic packages out of vending machines. These so-called foods are filled with artificial ingredients and simple carbs that encourage your body to store fat. The snack recipes you'll find in this book are made of only wholesome ingredients that taste great and provide you with real fuel for your day. Real Healthy Entrees: Dinner is when many people go a little crazy and make some bad decisions. Let's face it, after a long day it's comforting to have a nice dinner that tastes great. Unfortunately, the most popular entrées that restaurants serve are filled with more calories than you need, leaving your body primed and ready to store fat. The entrees you'll find in this book are filled with healthy sources of protein and lots of fiber-filled veggies. This is a winning combination for healthy weight loss. Take the time to read through all of the recipes and then roll up your sleeves and make a delicious fat burning meal for your family. You'll be surprised how delicious healthy food can be. Onward!

Real Healthy Breakfast Recipes

Real Healthy Donuts

These gorgeous breakfast treats are gluten-free, cane sugar-free and baked!

There's something *so* fun and satisfying about taking something that's *supposed* to be unhealthy and turning it into a wholesome snack.

Real Healthy Basic Donut recipe:

Dry ingredients:

- 1 1/4 cup blanched almond flour

- 1/4 teaspoon baking soda

Wet ingredients:

- 3 Tablespoons pure maple syrup, grade B

- 1 teaspoon apple cider vinegar
- 1/4 teaspoon almond extract
- 2 eggs, at room temperature, whites and
- 1/2 teaspoon vanilla extract yolks separated
- 2 Tablespoons coconut oil, melted

1. Preheat oven to 350 degrees F. Generously grease your 6-mold donut pan with coconut oil.

2. Combine the dry ingredients in a medium bowl. In another medium bowl combine all of the wet ingredients except egg whites.

3. Mix the wet with dry and set aside.

4. Beat the egg whites until firm peaks form. Gently fold the egg whites into the batter.

5. Equally distribute the batter between the 6 donut molds. Smooth out the tops of each donut. Bake for 1215 minutes until lightly golden.

6. Allow the donuts to cool, remove from pan and then chill in the fridge for half an hour.

12 HALF-DONUT SERVINGS
Nutritional Analysis: 111 calories, 8g fat, 32mg sodium, 4g carbohydrate, 2g fiber, and 4g protein

Real Healthy Chocolate Glazed Donut:

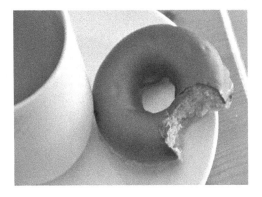

For the glaze:
- 1/2 cup very dark chocolate (73% cocoa)

- 1/4 cup unsweetened chocolate

- 2 Tablespoons coconut oil

1. Make the **Real Healthy Basic Donut Recipe** above.

2. For the Glaze: Fill a medium skillet with a few inches of water and place over medium-low heat. Place the glaze ingredients in a small saucepan and put the saucepan inside the skillet. Gently mix the ingredients until fully melted.

3. Pour the melted chocolate into a shallow bowl. Dip each chilled donut in the chocolate, then immediately chill for 30 minutes until the glaze hardens.

12 HALF-DONUT SERVINGS

Nutritional Analysis: One serving equals: 203 calories, 19g fat, 32mg sodium, 8g carbohydrate, 3g fiber, and 5g protein

Real Healthy Apple Fritter Donut

Add to the dry ingredients:

- 1/2 teaspoon ground cinnamon

Add to the wet ingredients:

- 1/4 teaspoon maple extract

Apple Fritter ingredients:

- 1 Tablespoon coconut oil
- 1 small, organic apple, finely chopped
- 1 Tablespoon maple syrup, grade B
- 1 teaspoon ground cinnamon
- 2 Tablespoons pecans, finely chopped

- 2 Tablespoons golden raisins

1. In a small skillet, heat the coconut oil over medium. Add the finely chopped apple and cook, stirring often until very soft, about 5 minutes. Add the syrup, cinnamon, pecans and raisins. Continue to cook for another 2 minutes. Remove from heat and allow to cool.

2. Make the **Real Healthy Basic Donut Recipe** above, mixing the cooled apple fritter ingredients to the dough in step Three.

12 HALF-DONUT SERVINGS

Nutritional Analysis: One serving equals: 145 calories, 10g fat, 32mg sodium, 8g carbohydrate, 2g fiber, and 4g protein

Apple Fritter Muffins

When I was little I loved apple fritters. The gooey, sticky, apple-y doughnut was my favorite thing to eat on Saturday mornings. Well, since traditional apple fritters are filled with sugar, unhealthy fats, carbs, and gluten, eating one just isn't an option anymore.

This recipe for Apple Fritter Muffins captures the flavor and experience of an apple fritter doughnut without any of the repercussions! In fact you'll be getting protein and even some fiber from these tasty treats.

Here's what you need for 12:

- 1 Tablespoon coconut oil
- 1 Tablespoon pure grade B maple syrup
- 2 organic apples, chopped

Real Healthy Breakfast Recipes

- 9 organic cage-free eggs

- 1/4 cup organic golden raisins

- 3 Tablespoons unsweetened coconut milk

- 1/4 cup pecans, chopped

- 1 1/2 Tablespoons coconut flour

- 4 Tablespoons water

- 1/4 teaspoon baking soda

- 1 Tablespoon ground cinnamon plus a dash

- dash of salt

1. Preheat oven to 350 degrees F. Lightly grease a 12-muffin pan with coconut oil.

2. In a skillet heat the coconut oil over medium. Add the apples, raisins, pecans, water, cinnamon and maple syrup. Cook, mixing often until the apples become tender. Remove from heat and allow to cool.

3. In a bowl combine the eggs, coconut milk, coconut flour, baking soda, dash of cinnamon and salt. Add two thirds of the apple mixture to the eggs. Mix until well combined.

4. Using a 1/4 cup, fill each prepared muffin tin with the egg mixture. Place a spoonful of the reserved apple mixture on top of each muffin.

5. Bake for 35 minutes, or until fully set.

12 SERVINGS

Nutritional Analysis: One serving equals: 117 calories, 7g fat, 84mg sodium, 7g carbohydrate, 2g fiber, and 6g protein

Blueberry & Lemon Mini Muffins

When you make the decision to be healthier, by cutting gluten, sugar and dairy from your diet, your body responds immediately.

You feel lighter, tighter, and energetic.

You grow accustomed to breakfasts of eggs, meat, nuts and berries...until one day you have an intense craving for blueberry muffins.

That's when this recipe saves the day 😃

Here's what you need for 24 mini muffins:

- 6 eggs

- 1/2 cup coconut flour

- 1/2 cup coconut oil, melted over low heat

- 1/2 teaspoon salt
- 1 teaspoon vanilla extract
- 1/4 teaspoon baking soda
- 1/4 teaspoon almond extract
- 1 cup organic, fresh blueberries
- 1/4 cup grade B maple syrup
- 1/4 cup sliced almonds
- 1 lemon, zest and juice

1. Preheat oven to 350 degrees F. Grease a mini muffin pan with coconut oil

2. In a medium bowl combine the eggs, melted (and cooled) coconut oil, vanilla and almond extract, maple syrup, lemon juice and zest.

3. In a small bowl, whisk the coconut flour to remove lumps, add salt and baking soda.

4. Mix the dry ingredients into the wet ones, then gently fold in the blueberries.

5. Fill each mini muffin tin to the top, then sprinkle with sliced almonds.

6. Bake for 30 minutes, then turn on the broil for 1-2 minutes (watch close!) to lightly brown the tops.

7. Allow to cool before removing from muffin tin. Store in an airtight container in the fridge for up to a week.

24 SERVINGS

Nutritional Analysis: One serving equals: 84 calories, 5g fat, 55mg sodium, 4g carbohydrate, 1g fiber, and 2g protein

Baked Pumpkin French Toast Coffee Cake

This yummy, wholesome-cheat, recipe is my rebuttal to the pumpkin spice latte. It's part French Toast, part coffee cake streusel, and part pumpkin custard.

While this may initially sound like a weird combination — it works deliciously!

Enjoy a gourmet slice of fall...this may even taste better than pumpkin pie!

Here's what you need for 10 servings:

- 1 Tablespoon coconut oil
- 1/2 cup organic pumpkin puree
- 5 slices sprouted grain bread

- 1/3 cup coconut crystals

- 4 omega 3 eggs

- 1 teaspoon vanilla extract

- 2 egg whites

For the Streusel Topping:

- 1/2 cup almond meal

- 1/4 teaspoon salt

- 1/4 cup coconut crystals

- 2 Tablespoons coconut oil

- 1 teaspoon pumpkin pie spice

1. Melt the coconut oil in an 8-inch oven-friendly skillet. Coat the entire pan, including the sides. Remove from heat.

2. Slice the sprouted grain bread diagonally. Place the bread slices, cut side down, and point side up across the pan.

3. In a medium sized bowl, combine the eggs, egg whites, pumpkin puree, coconut crystals and vanilla extract. Mix well. Pour the mixture over the bread slices, coating each side of each slice. The skillet will be nearly filled with the pumpkin mixture.

4. Cover the skillet with plastic wrap and refrigerate for 30 minutes to overnight.

5. Preheat your oven to 350 degrees F.

6. Combine the Streusel topping ingredients in a small bowl. Remove the skillet from refrigerator and crumble the streusel topping over the soaked bread slices.

7. Bake for 25 to 30 minutes, until the custard has set and the tops of the bread slices are toasted. Allow to cool for 15 minutes. Slice and enjoy!

10 SERVINGS

Nutritional Analysis: One serving equals: 140 calories, 9g fat, 95mg sodium, 10g carbohydrate, 1g fiber, and 5g protein

Greens, Eggs and Ham

Who doesn't love breakfast that comes in a cute package? I certainly do.

These Greens, Eggs and Ham cups are perfect for your healthy on-the-go breakfast!

First fill your ham cups with veggies.

Here's what you need for 12 servings:

- 1 teaspoon olive oil
- 1 cup broccoli, steamed and chopped
- 1 clove garlic, minced
- 1/4 cup shredded cheddar cheese
- 1/2 yellow onion, chopped
- dash of salt and pepper

- 12 slices of nitrate free ham
- 12 eggs

1. Preheat oven to 350 degrees F. Lightly spray a muffin pan with nonstick cooking spray. Set aside

2. In a medium sized skillet, heat the olive oil over medium heat. Add the garlic and onions. Cook until tender.

3. Add the steamed broccoli, cheese, salt and pepper. Mix until fully combined. Remove from heat.

4. Using kitchen scissors, make a slice to the center of each piece of ham, then fold into a cone shape in each muffin cup. Fill halfway with the broccoli mixture.

5. Crack an egg into each ham cup. Bake for 16-20 minutes, or until the edges of the ham are crispy.

12 SERVINGS

Nutritional Analysis: One serving equals: 135 calories, 8g fat, 437mg sodium, 2g carbohydrate, 1g fiber, and 12g protein.

Low Carb Green Smoothie

There are days that call for the cleansing power of greens –you know what I'm talking about.

Here's what you need for 2 servings:

- 1 cup coconut water
- 1 Tablespoon almond butter
- 1/4 cup wheat grass
- 2 cups spinach
- 1 scoop high quality, low carb chocolate protein
- 1 inch slice of banana
- Optional pinch of Stevia

- 1/2 cup ice

1. Combine all the ingredients in your high speed blender then blend on high for a full minute, or until the tiny pieces of spinach have disappeared and the smoothie turns a brilliant shade of green.

2 SERVINGS

Nutritional Analysis: One serving equals: 155 calories, 4g fat, 105mg sodium, 15g carbohydrate, 2g fiber, and 15g protein.

Real Healthy
Cinnamon Swirl
Bread

This version of the classic almond bread loaf has a fun swirl of cinnamon and raisins. Just like you're having a cinnamon roll!

Here's what you need for 30 half-slices:

- 5 cups blanched almond flour
- 2 Tablespoons agave nectar
- 1 teaspoon baking soda
- 2 teaspoons apple cider vinegar
- 1/2 teaspoon salt
- 1/3 cup golden raisins

- 1 teaspoon cinnamon

- 1/2 cup ground walnuts

- 6 omega-3, free range eggs

- 1 Tablespoon cinnamon

1. Preheat oven to 300 degrees F. Grease a loaf pan with coconut oil.

2. In a medium sized bowl combine the almond flour, baking soda, salt and cinnamon.

3. In another bowl combine the eggs, agave nectar and vinegar. Mix well.

4. Pour the wet ingredients over the dry and mix until just combined. Mix in the raisins.

5. In a small bowl combine the ground walnuts and cinnamon.

6. Generously cover a cutting board with almond flour. Place the dough on the floured surface and carefully pat out into a large rectangle, about an inch thick, with a length that matches the length of your loaf pan. Evenly cover the dough with the walnut and cinnamon mixture.

7. Carefully, using extra almond flour as needed, roll the dough up (keeping the same length as your loaf pan), then use a spatula to lift the rolled dough and drop into the loaf pan.

8. Bake for 45-60 minutes, until a toothpick comes out clean. Allow to cool in the pan for 30 minutes.

30 SERVINGS

One serving equals: 149 calories, 11g fat, 50mg sodium, 7g carbohydrate, 2g fiber, and 6g protein.

Real Healthy Chocolate Chip Pancakes (Gluten Free)

If someone held a gun to my head and told me to choose only one thing to eat for the rest of my life, this would be the thought bubble above my head...

"Cookies.....Pancakes....Cookies....Pancakes....Cookies....Pancakes....Cookies....Pancakes...."

And in the end I'd choose this Chocolate Chip Pancake recipe!

Wholesome ingredients with a sprinkle of mini chocolate chips make this pancake recipe the most fun you'll ever try.

Here's what you need for 15 pancakes:

- 3 omega-3, free range eggs

- 1 1/2 cup blanched almond meal

- 1 Tablespoon agave nectar

- 1/2 teaspoon salt

- 1 Tablespoon vanilla extract

- 1/2 teaspoon baking soda

- 1/2 cup coconut milk (full fat, from a can)

- 1/3 cup mini chocolate chips

- 2 Tablespoon flax meal

- 1 Tablespoon coconut oil

1. In a blender combine the eggs, agave nectar, vanilla and coconut milk. Blend until smooth. Add the flax, almond flour, salt and baking soda. Blend until smooth. Fold the chocolate chips into the batter.

2. Grease a large skillet or pancaked griddle with coconut oil and place over medium heat. Place heaping tablespoons of batter onto the skillet and cook until bubbles form. Flip each pancake and cook for another minute, until golden on both sides.

15 SERVINGS

One serving equals: 119 calories, 9g fat, 52mg sodium, 5g carbohydrate, 2g fiber, and 4g protein

Orange Blueberry Paleo Muffins

whenever I bite into a big, juicy blueberry it brings me back to late-summer trips down to the blueberry farm.

The sweet-tart flavor of blueberry pairs perfectly with refreshing orange. These muffins are low carb, proteinfilled and delicately flavored. Enjoy one for an energizing power breakfast.

Here's what you need for 12 muffins:

- 3 cups blanched almond flour

- 1/4 cup fresh squeezed orange juice

- 1/4 teaspoon salt

- 1/4 cup coconut oil, melted over low heat

- 1 1/2 teaspoon baking soda

- 1/4 cup agave nectar

- 1 teaspoon ground cinnamon

- 1 Tablespoon orange zest

- 1 Tablespoon flax meal

- 1/2 teaspoon vanilla extract

- 3 omega-3, free range eggs

- 1 1/2 cup fresh blueberries

1. Preheat oven to 325 degrees F. Generously grease 12 muffin tin pan with coconut oil.

2. In a medium bowl combine the almond flour, salt, baking soda, flax meal, and cinnamon. Mix until well combined.

3. In a large bowl combine the eggs, orange juice, agave nectar, coconut oil, orange zest and vanilla. Mix until well combined.

4. Add the dry ingredients to the wet ones in small batches, mix until fully incorporated. Fold in the blueberries.

5. Fill the prepared muffin tin and bake for 30-35 minutes, until golden.

24 SERVINGS

One serving equals: 128 calories, 10g fat, 93mg sodium, 7g carbohydrate, 2g fiber, and 4g protein.

Low-Carb Lemon Poppyseed Sunshine Bread

This low carb Lemon Poppyseed Sunshine Bread lets its true self shine with every bite. Unadulterated lemon flavor, nutritious poppy seeds and buttery almond flour create a pure and honest treat.

Here's what you need for 24 servings:

- 1 teaspoon chia seeds plus 3 Tablespoons
- 1/3 cup coconut oil, melted over low heat filtered water
- 2 Tablespoons lemon rind
- 5 cups blanched almond flour
- 1/3 cup agave nectar
- 1 teaspoon baking soda

- 1/2 teaspoon almond extract

- 1/2 teaspoon salt

- 1/2 teaspoon vanilla extract

- 5 omega-3, free range eggs

- 1 Tablespoon poppy seeds

1. Preheat oven to 300 degrees F. Generously grease a loaf pan with coconut oil. Set aside.

2. In a small cup combine the chia seeds and filtered water. Mix well and set aside (after 15 minutes it will become jelly-like).

3. In a medium bowl combine the blanched almond flour, baking soda and salt.

4. In a large bowl combine the eggs, coconut oil, lemon rind, agave nectar and extracts. Gently mix in the chia seed mixture.

5. Mix the wet and dry ingredients together. Fold in the poppy seeds, then transfer the batter to prepared loaf pan. Smooth the top of the loaf.

6. Bake for 45-60 minutes, until a toothpick inserted in the center comes out clean.

7. Allow to cool in the pan for 1 hour before slicing.

24 SERVINGS

One serving equals: 189 calories, 15g fat, 92mg sodium, 8g carbohydrate, 3g fiber, and 7g protein.

Real Healthy Pancakes

There's nothing quite as nice as a lazy Saturday.

The only way to make a lazy Saturday even more perfect is to start it with pancakes. This recipe for Real Healthy Pancakes is filled with protein and is low in carbs and sugar.

Don't even think about using a corn syrup or refined sugar filled topping. Stick with pure maple syrup and sliced fresh fruit.

Here's what you need for 10 servings:

- 3 large omega-3, free range eggs
- 1 1/2 cups blanched almond flour
- 1 Tablespoon agave nectar

- 1/2 teaspoon salt

- 1 Tablespoon vanilla extract

- 1/2 teaspoon baking soda

- 1/2 cup filtered water

- coconut oil

- 2 Tablespoons flax meal

1. In a blender combine the eggs, agave nectar, vanilla and water. Mix until smooth. Add the flax, almond flour, salt and baking soda. Mix until well combined.

2. Grease a large skillet or pancaked griddle with coconut oil and place over medium heat. Place heaping tablespoons of batter onto the skillet and cook until bubbles form. Flip each pancake and cook for another minute, until golden on both sides.

10 Servings

Nutritional Analysis: One serving equals: 137 calories, 10g fat, 153mg sodium, 6g carbohydrate, 2g fiber, and 6g protein.

Real Healthy Puff Pancake

Puff pancakes are probably the easiest pancakes to make since you just pour all the batter into a pie pan and bake it for 20 minutes — no flipping necessary.

Here's what you need:

- 2 Tablespoons organic butter
- 1/2 cup low fat cottage cheese
- 1/2 cup non-fat Greek yogurt
- 1 cup almond meal
- 1/2 cup water
- 1 teaspoon baking powder
- 6 organic, omega 3, free range eggs

- 1/2 teaspoon salt

- 2 Tablespoons raw honey

1. Preheat oven to 425 degrees F. Place butter in a pie plate and melt in the oven.

2. Place all the remaining ingredients in blender and blend for 1 minute. Pour batter into pie plate.

3. Bake until puffy and golden, about 20 minutes. Cut into wedges and serve with fresh strawberries an pure maple syrup.

10 Servings

Nutritional Analysis: One serving equals: 155 calories, 11g fat, 203mg sodium, 7g carbohydrate, 1.2g fiber, and 9g protein.

Real Healthy Snacks

Real Healthy
Plantain Chips

Before I started eating only real, wholesome and unprocessed foods I used to occasionally snack on a salty bag of fried plantain chips. You know the ones — fried in vegetable oil and doused in salt and preservatives. Not what you'd call very healthy, although quite tasty.

These days I do not eat packaged snack, as a part of my commitment to eat only real food in 2013. So when I walked past a pile of plantains at the market I had the bright idea to create my own crunchy snack, baked and not fried.

This recipe is sooooo simple, and the result is a delicious, sinfully crunchy snack.

Here's what you need:

- 2 large unripe plantains
- olive oil
- juice from 1/2 a lemon
- freshly ground sea salt

1. Preheat the oven to 350 degrees F. Lightly grease 2 large baking sheets with olive oil.

2. Peel the plantains and slice thinly on a diagonal. In a medium bowl toss the plantains with some olive oil, the juice from 1/2 a lemon and a generous sprinkle of salt.

3. Arrange in a single layer on the prepared baking sheets. Bake for 30 minutes, or until golden and crisp.

6 servings

Nutritional Analysis: One serving equals: 110 calories, 2g fat, 133mg sodium, 22g carbohydrate, 2g fiber, and 1g protein

Real Healthy Crackers

Here's a fun snack that tastes like a cheat food, but is actually in line with my Real Healthy Recipes Eating Guidelines.

Even though these are dairy-free, the taste reminds me of Cheez-It crackers.

These crackers are crunchiest when right out of the oven — once you store them in the fridge they soften.

Here's what you need:

- 1/2 cup blanched almond flour
- 1 omega-3, free range egg
- 1/4 cup coconut flour
- 1 Tablespoon coconut oil, melted
- 1/4 teaspoon sea salt

41

- 1 Tablespoon tomato paste
- 1 teaspoon dried basil
- olive oil and sea salt for garnish
- 1 packet stevia

1. Preheat oven to 350 degrees F. Line a baking sheet with wax paper.

2. In a medium bowl combine the almond flour, coconut flour, salt, basil and stevia.

3. Add the egg and mix well. Add the coconut oil and tomato paste, mix with your hands.

4. Place the dough on the prepared pan. Top with another piece of wax paper, and press into a rectangle that is about 1/8 inch thick. Be careful not to let the edges get too thin.

5. Use a knife to carefully cut the dough into 30 crackers – 6 lengthwise slices and 5 crosswise sections. Sprinkle with olive oil and sea salt.

6. Bake for 15 minutes, or until the crackers are golden.

7. Cool on the tray and then enjoy. Store leftovers in an airtight container in the fridge.

30 CRACKERS

Serving size= 5 crackers. Nutritional Analysis: One serving equals: 118 calories, 8g fat, 83mg sodium, 5g carbohydrate, 3g fiber, and 4g protein

Andrew's Fun Dip

My 7 year old son, Andrew, loves a challenge.

The other day he casually posed the question, "Mom, could you make any food into a healthy recipe?"

Well, mommy likes a challenge too, so I puffed out my chest and said, "Of course I can!"

He smiled and came back with, "Ok, how about Fun Dip?"

For those of you who don't have school aged children, Fun Dip is a packaged candy that's basically pure sugar with artificial colors and flavors. It has a candy stick that is dipped into colorful sugar, licked off and then dipped again. You know, the atrocious kind of thing that kids end up with after a birthday party or Halloween.

Well, I took Andrew's challenge and ended up with a fun,

wholesome snack that's quick to make and entertaining to eat!

Here's what you need:

- 1 oz bag freeze dried strawberries
- 1/2 a jicama, peeled and sliced

1. Throw the freeze dried fruit into a food processor and blend until it becomes a fine powder. (Make sure you remove that little stay-fresh packet before blending!)

2. Serve the powdered fruit in a small bowl or ziplock bag with a handful of jicama sticks.

2 SERVINGS

Nutritional Analysis: 149 calories, .2g fat, 11mg sodium, 32g carbohydrate, 14g fiber, and 3g protein

Maui Wowi Bars

Maui is by far our favorite place to vacation.

These sweet bars combine two of my favorite Maui indulgences — tender, sweet mango and buttery, salted macadamia nuts.

One bite of this treat and you'll hear the ocean waves in your ear.

Here's what you need:

- 1 cup dried, unsweetened mango
- 2 Tablespoons flax meal
- 2 cups roasted, salted macadamia nuts
- 1/2 teaspoon ground ginger

- 2 Tablespoons sesame seeds

- 1/4 teaspoon ground cinnamon

- 1/4 cup roasted, salted sunflower seeds

- 1/4 cup coconut oil

- 1/4 cup shredded, unsweetened coconut,

- 1 Tablespoon raw honey plus 2 Tablespoons

1. Preheat oven to 325 degrees F. Place parchment paper in the bottom of a 8×8 inch pan, and rub with melted coconut oil.

2. Place the dried mango in a bowl of hot water, and allow to sit for 15 minutes. Drain the water and chop the mango into small pieces.

3. Combine the macnuts, sesame seeds, sunflower seeds, 1/4 cup of the shredded coconut, flax meal, ginger, and cinnamon in a food processor. Pulse until fine and well combined.

4. In a saucepan over very low heat, melt the coconut oil and raw honey. Turn the food processor back on and drizzle the coconut oil mixture in. Allow to mix until fully incorporated.

5. Transfer the dough to a medium bowl. Carefully mix in the mango pieces.

6. Press the dough evenly into prepared pan then sprinkle with the remaining 2 Tablespoons of coconut.

7. Bake for 25-30 minutes until the top is golden. Allow to cool for 20 minutes in the pan, then transfer the entire pan to the fridge to chill before cutting into bars.

8. Serve and enjoy.

24 Bars

Nutritional Analysis: 143 calories, 13g fat, 36g sodium, 6g carbohydrate, 2g fiber, and 2g protein

Real Healthy Granola Bars

Yay! Here's a wholesome version of the packaged-and-pumped-full-of-sugar-and-gluten granola bars that the kids love!

Whole seeds, nuts, shredded coconut and mini chocolate chips combined with almond butter, flax meal, coconut oil and maple syrup make these bars super tasty and fully loaded with vitamins, minerals, and real, usable calories.

Here's what you need:

- 2 Tablespoons ground flax meal

- 1/2 cup raw pumpkin seeds

- 3 Tablespoons filtered water

- 1/2 cup roasted, salted sunflower seeds

- 1/3 cup coconut oil, melted
- 1/2 cup sliced almonds
- 1/4 cup pure maple syrup, grade b
- 1/2 cup mini dairy-free, soy-free chocolate
- 1/2 cup almond butter (no sugar added) chips
- 1/4 teaspoon almond extract
- 1/2 cup unsweetened, shredded coconut

1. Preheat oven to 325 degrees F. Line the bottom of a 8×8 inch pan with parchment paper, and coat with coconut oil. Set aside.

2. In a small cup combine the flax meal and water. Whisk with a fork and set aside to thicken.

3. In a small saucepan, over low heat, combine the coconut oil, maple syrup, almond butter and almond extract. Stir occasionally and remove from heat when melted. Allow to cool, about 10 minutes.

4. Add the thickened flax meal to the saucepan and mix to combine.

5. In a medium bowl, combine the seeds, nuts, coconut and chocolate chips. Pour the almond butter mixture in and mix well. Press the mixture into the prepared pan.

6. Bake for 25-35 minutes, until golden and bubbly. Remove from oven and allow to cool in the pan for 15 minutes.

7. Once cooled, loosen the sides with a knife, then invert onto a cutting board. Remove the parchment paper by peeling off carefully. Place the entire cutting board into the fridge for 15 minutes — this is an important step that will ensure that your bars harden completely and do not crumble. After 15 minutes, remove from fridge and cut into 20 bars. Store in an airtight container in the fridge.

20 Servings

Nutritional Analysis: One serving equals: 171 calories, 14g fat, 2mg sodium, 9g carbohydrate, 2g fiber, and 4g protein

Easy Kale Chips, The Classic and The Cheesy

Alright friends, we've cut the pesky grains out of our diets.... so now what do we have to snack on that's salty and crunchy?

Kale chips!!!!!!

If you're new to kale chips I do NOT blame you for being skeptical. I mean kale was created to fill the gaps of a salad bar, right? Decorative greens. That's what I used to think 😃 Actually kale makes a delicious crunchy, salty snack to much on. A snack that won't increase your waistline or negatively impact your health.

Below are two different recipes. I love the cheesy ones, but you can't go wrong with the classic.

Here's what you need:

The Classic
- 1 bunch kale, washed and torn, stems discarded

The Cheesy
- 1 Tablespoon olive oil dash of salt and pepper

- 1 bunch kale, washed and torn, stems discarded

- 1 Tablespoon olive oil

- dash of salt and pepper 3/4 cup nutritional yeast

- 1/4 cup blanched almond flour

1. Preheat oven to 300 degrees F.

2. In a large bowl mix the kale pieces with all of the ingredients.

3. Spread evenly on foil-lined baking sheets.

4. Bake for 12 minutes, watching closely that they do not burn. Remove from oven when crispy.

5 SERVINGS

Classic: 51 calories, 3g fat, 68mg sodium, 5g carbohydrate, 1g fiber, and 2g protein

Cheesy: 180 calories, 7g fat, 77mg sodium, 17g carbohydrate, 7g fiber, and 15g protein

Easy Baked Meatballs

Have you noticed how almost all snack foods are bad for you? It's like there's a law that anything quick and easy to grab has to be filled with carbohydrates or straight up sugar.

Until now.

These Easy Baked Meatballs are the perfect, anti-high-carb snack to enjoy on a busy afternoon.

This is also makes for a healthy, quick week-night dinner.

Here's what you need:

- 2 lbs ground pork
- 2 teaspoons coconut oil
- 1/2 teaspoon salt

- 2 cloves garlic, minced

- 1/2 teaspoon ground fennel

- 1 small onion, finely chopped

- 1/4 teaspoon ground sage

- 2 celery stalks, finely chopped

- 1/4 teaspoon onion powder

- 2 carrots, finely chopped

- 1/4 teaspoon garlic powder

- 1/4 cup pecans, finely chopped

- dash of pepper

- 1/4 cup fresh parsley, finely chopped

1. Preheat oven to 425 degrees F.

2. In a medium bowl combine the ground pork with all of the spices. Don't be afraid to get your hands dirty!

3. Place a skillet over medium heat and warm the coconut oil. Add the garlic, onion, celery, carrots, pecans and parsley. Cook for about 3 minutes, until soft. Set the mixture aside to cool.

4. Add the vegetable mixture into the ground pork and combine well. Use your hands to form golf ball sized meatballs.

5. Place the meatballs in an oven-safe baking dish. Bake for 30 minutes, or until cooked all the way through.

24 Meatballs

Nutritional Analysis: One serving equals: 77 calories, 4g fat, 76mg sodium, 1g carbohydrate, .5g fiber, and 8g protein

Apricot Loaf with Orange Glaze

I am a total believer in the health benefits of a diet with no grains or refined sugars. In fact I eat this way, and have for quite some time now. But on the other hand I LOVE to bake... there was no chance that I'd give up baking. The good news is that with a few ingredient substitutions it is more than possible to create delicious, moist and sweet baked goods all while sticking to a grain-free and refined-sugar-free diet.

This Apricot Loaf with Orange Glaze is delicately sweet and perfect to enjoy with a cup of tea.

Here's what you need:

For the Bread:
- 5 cups almond meal (buy at Trader Joe's- 4

- 6 omega-3, free range eggs cups in each bag, or grind raw almonds in food processor)

- 4 Tablespoons raw honey

- 2 teaspoons apple cider vinegar

- 1 heaping teaspoon baking soda

- 1/2 teaspoon vanilla extract

- 1/2 teaspoon salt

- 1/2 cup dried apricots, finely chopped

- 1/2 teaspoon ground cinnamon

- 1/3 cup pecans, finely chopped

- 1/8 teaspoon ground cloves

1. Preheat oven to 300 degrees F. Generously grease a loaf pan with coconut oil.

2. In a large bowl combine the almond meal, baking soda, salt, cinnamon and cloves.

3. In a separate bowl, whisk eggs then add honey, vinegar, vanilla. Add the wet ingredients to dry ones and mix until combined.

4. Gently fold in the apricots and pecans.

5. Fill prepared loaf pan, smooth the top of the dough. Bake for 45 mins or until golden brown.

6. Loosen side of bread immediately after removing from oven, then allow to cool completely before removing

from pan.

7. Place the loaf in the freezer for 20 minutes before applying the glaze.

For the Glaze:
- 3 Tablespoons coconut oil, melted

- 1/4 teaspoon vanilla extract

- 3 Tablespoons coconut butter, softened

- zest from an orange

- 1 Tablespoon raw honey, melted

1. pour the glaze over the top and smooth it out, allowing glaze to drip down the sides.

Making the glaze work: The coconut ingredients in the glaze are hard when cold, so to make your glaze work it's important to keep your loaf cold, and to store your loaf in the fridge once glazed.

24 Servings

Nutritional Analysis: One serving equals: 204 calories, 15g fat, 98mg sodium, 11g carbohydrate, 3.5g fiber, and 8g protein

Quinoa Minty Fruit Salad

Quinoa is quite the superfood. Often mistaken for a grain, quinoa is actually a protein-packed seed. It's gluten free (yay!) and is a complete protein, containing all 9 essential amino acids. It is also filled with magnesium and fiber, as if the other benefits weren't enough to convince us.

The one drawback to this amazing food is the carbohydrate volume. While it is lower than rice or other traditional grains, it is high enough that you'll want to limit the amount you eat.

Of course the kids need plenty of carbohydrates to support their active, growing bodies!

Most quinoa recipes are savory, so this minty, fruity salad is a refreshing twist on the nutritious-packed superfood.

Here's what you need for 6 servings:

- 3/4 cup plain greek yogurt
- 1 cup blueberries
- 2 Tablespoons lime juice, divided
- 1 cup green grapes, halved
- 1-15 fresh mint leaves, minced
- 1/2 cup raspberries
- 2 cups cooked quinoa
- 1 Tablespoon agave nectar
- dash of salt and pepper

1. In a small bowl combine the yogurt, 1 tablespoon lime juice and the mint. Pour over the cooked quinoa and mix well. Season with salt and pepper.

2. In another bowl combine the fruit, agave nectar and remaining lime juice.

3. Cover and refrigerate each bowl for 2 hours, to allow the flavors to emerge, then combine the fruit with the quinoa and serve.

6 Servings

Nutritional Analysis: One serving equals: 139 calories, 1g fat, 114mg sodium, 27g carbohydrate, 3g fiber, and 6g protein.

Real Healthy Trail Mix

Trail mix is my favorite vacation food.

It's perfect to throw into your bag for a road trip or airplane ride.

The problem with store bought trail mix lurks in the fine print on the back of the package. Added sugar, chemicals and preservatives spoil even the most natural trail mix brands.

This Real Healthy Trail Mix takes only the most pure and healthy ingredients and toasts them into sweet perfection.

Here's what you need:

- 1 teaspoon Chia seeds plus 3 Tablespoons
- 1 cup sliced almonds, raw and unsalted filtered water

- 1 cup pecans, raw and unsalted

- 2 Tablespoons raw honey, melted

- 1 cup pistachio nutmeats, unsalted

- 1/2 teaspoon vanilla extract

- 1 cup dried blueberries, unsweetened

- 1/2 teaspoon almond extract

- 1/2 cup sesame seeds

- 2 Tablespoon coconut oil, melted

- 1 cup large, unsweetened coconut flakes

1. Mix the chia seeds and water in a small cup and set aside for 15 minutes, until it becomes gel-like.

2. Preheat oven to 375 degrees F. Generously grease a baking pan with coconut oil.

3. In a small bowl combine the honey, extracts, coconut oil and chia seed mixture.

4. In a large bowl combine the nuts, berries, seeds and coconut flakes. Mix in the wet ingredients until well combined.

5. Spread over the prepared baking sheet. Bake for 10 minutes, stir, and then bake for another 10 minutes until evenly golden.

24 servings

Nutritional Analysis: One serving equals: 160 calories, 12g fat, 2mg sodium, 11g carbohydrate, 4g fiber, and 4g protein

Real Healthy Entrees

Lamb and Apricot Slow Cooker Stew

Cooking lamb was completely new to me, and I'll admit that I was a little nervous going into this recipe. With the majority of the cooking down in the slow cooker, my lamb turned out perfect — tenderly falling off the bone.

If you've never cooked lamb, give it a shot! You might find that it's your new favorite.

Here's what you need:

- 2 Tablespoons coconut oil, divided
- 2 pounds lamb meat, bone-in
- 2 yellow onions, thinly sliced
- 32 oz organic beef broth
- 5 carrots, sliced into rounds

- 1 Tablespoon lemon juice

- 1 sweet potato, peeled and cubed

- 2 Tablespoons fresh dill, minced

- 2 cloves garlic, minced

- 1/4 cup fresh parsley, minced

- 1 Tablespoon fresh ginger, minced

- 1 teaspoon dried basil

- 2 Anaheim chili peppers, seeded and diced

- salt and pepper

- 6oz dried apricots, chopped

1. In a large skillet melt one Tablespoon of the coconut oil over medium high heat. Add the onions, carrots, sweet potato, garlic, ginger, chili pepper and apricots. Sauté for 10 minutes and then transfer everything to the slow cooker.

2. Salt and pepper the lamb. Add a Tablespoon of coconut oil to the skillet and brown the lamb, about 6 minutes. Transfer the lamb to the slow cooker.

3. In a medium bowl combine the broth, lemon juice, and remaining fresh and dried herbs. Mix well then pour into the slow cooker.

4. Cook on low for 6 to 8 hours. Salt and pepper to taste and then serve.

8 SERVINGS

Nutritional Analysis: One serving equals: 352 calories, 12g fat, 418mg sodium, 25g carbohydrate, 4g fiber, and 36g protein.

Caveman MeatBall Sub

When your meals are grain-free it can feel like every night you're looking at a piece of meat with a pile of greens. Not that there's anything wrong with meat and greens, but sometimes it's fun to have a unique dish that still steers clear of grains, gluten and starch.

Here's what you need:

For the MeatBalls:
- 1 pound grass-fed ground beef

- 1/2 teaspoon smoked paprika

- 1 pound organic ground turkey

- 1/2 teaspoon dried basil

- 1 cup yellow onion, finely chopped

- 1/2 teaspoon dried rosemary

- 3 cloves garlic, minced

- 1/2 teaspoon ground black pepper

- 1/4 cup fresh parsley, chopped

- 2 Tablespoons coconut flour

- 1/2 teaspoon sea salt

- 2 Tablespoons almond meal

- 1 teaspoon dried oregano

- Olive oil for cooking

For the Sauce:
- 1 Tablespoon olive oil

- 3 Tablespoons fresh parsley, chopped

- 1/4 cup yellow onion, minced

- 1/2 teaspoon smoked paprkia

- 1 clove garlic, minced

- 1 jar organic, marinara sauce

1. Bake a loaf of Almond Bread using blanched almond flour. Once cooled, cut into thick slices.

2. For the Meatballs: Combine all of the meatball ingredients in a bowl, mix it all up with your hands until fully combined. Form 1.5 inch balls.

3. Place some olive oil in a large skillet over medium high heat. Evenly space the meatballs around the pan. After a few minutes turn the meatballs to brown on all sides.

4. For the Sauce: Place the olive oil in a medium saucepan over medium heat. Add the onion, garlic, parsley and paprika. Cook for a few minutes, stirring often. Add the jar of marinara and continue to heat for 5 minutes.

5. Assemble your Caveman MeatBall Subs: Place a slice of almond bread on each plate. Spread with some sauce, top with meat balls and more sauce.

6 Servings

Nutritional Analysis: One serving equals approx: 512 calories, 28g fat, 365mg sodium, 15g carbohydrate, 6g fiber, and 46g protein

Spice-Rubbed Chicken Breast & Moroccan Herb Dressing

I have 2 goals when cooking chicken breast for dinner, and this recipe meets them both.

My first goal is that the finished product be juicy, and not dry. There's nothing worse than trying to choke down dry chicken. This recipe calls for brining the chicken breast in a bag of water and spices, which locks moisture deep in the meat. I mention below to keep your grill closed while cooking, this also helps create a juicy piece of meat.

My second goal is that the finished product be filled with rich flavor. Bland chicken ranks right up there with dry chicken on the list of things I'd rather not eat. The spice rub in this recipe coats the chicken in savory flavor, and the Moroccan herb dressing adds another dimension.

Even though the ingredient list is long, if you look closely you'll see that it's mainly a bunch of spices, the whole process is quick and painless. Just remember to start your brining 2 hours before dinner, the rest comes together very quickly.

Here's what you need:

For the Brining:

- 2 garlic cloves, crushed
- 7 cups filtered water
- 2 Tablespoons salt
- 1 Tablespoon coconut aminos
- 1 bay leaf

For the Spice Rub:

- 1 teaspoon ground coriander
- 1 teaspoon ground cumin
- 1 teaspoon whole black peppercorns
- 2.5 pounds organic, skinless, boneless chicken breast
- 1 Tablespoon ground cumin
- 2 teaspoons curry powder
- 1 teaspoon chili powder
- 2 teaspoons allspice 1 teaspoon cinnamon
- 1 teaspoon black pepper
- 1 Tablespoon coconut oil, melted

For the Moroccan Herb Dressing:

- 1/4 cup lemon juice
- 1 garlic clove, minced
- 1/2 teaspoon cumin
- 2 teaspoons sweet paprika
- 1/2 teaspoon salt
- dash of pepper
- 1/4 cup olive oil
- 1/4 cup fresh cilantro, minced
- 1/4 cup fresh parsley, minced

1. For the Brining: Place all of the brining ingredients into a gallon-sized Ziplock bag. Add the chicken breasts. Place in the fridge for 2 full hours.

2. For the Spice Rub: Preheat your grill on high heat. Combine all of the spices in a small bowl and then add the melted coconut oil.

3. Remove the chicken from brine, rinse well and pat dry. Rub the spice mixture all over the chicken breasts. Place on the preheated grill for 4 minutes each side, with the lid closed. Remove once the chicken is cooked through.

4. For the Dressing: In a small bowl combine all of the ingredients together. Whisk until well combined.

5. Slice the cooked chicken breasts and top with a generous serving of dressing.

8 Servings

Nutritional Analysis: One serving equals: 244 calories, 12g fat, 657mg sodium, 2g carbohydrate, 1g fiber, and 30g protein

The World's Best Steak Salad

What do you do with that extra rib-eye steak leftover from last night's dinner? Turn it into the world's best steak salad of course.

This salad is filled with only wholesome, real food ingredients and delicious homemade dressing.

If you have leftover Real Healthy Steak Sauce then drizzle some of that over the steak as well!

Here's what you need:

For the Dressing:

- 1 clove garlic, minced

- 2 Tablespoon olive oil

- 1/2 teaspoon powdered stevia

- 2 Tablespoons fresh chives, minced

- juice from 1 lemon

- dash of salt and pepper

- 2 teaspoon balsamic vinegar

For the Salad

- 4 oz cooked and sliced rib-eye steak (grass-fed of course!)

- 1 avocado, sliced and dressed with lemon juice and sweet paprika

- 2 hard boiled eggs, sliced

- 6 green onions, grilled

- 1/2 cup cherry tomatoes, halved

- 4 cups mixed greens

1. Prepare your ingredients and set them aside, ready for salad assembly.

2. In a small bowl whisk together the dressing ingredients.

3. Arrange the greens on two plates, then top with the remaining salad ingredients. Drizzle with the dressing.

3 Servings

Nutritional Analysis: One serving equals: 364 calories, 28g fat, 110mg sodium, 13g carbohydrate, 7g fiber, and 15g protein

Grain-Free Dolmas

These dolmas are packed with flavor, not grains. Cauliflower rice takes the place of traditional rice, making this dish healthier and just as tasty.

I used an expedited cooking method –using an oven — however if you prefer to cook traditionally then do not pre-cook the meat and place the dolmas in a large pot with a couple cups of water on the stove for 2 hours, or until cooked through.

Here's what you need:

- 1 Tablespoon olive oil
- 1/4 teaspoon ground coriander
- 1 yellow onion, diced
- 12 prunes, finely minced

- 1 pound ground pork (or ground meat of your choice)

- 1 head cauliflower, shredded in food processor

- 2 gloves garlic, minced

- 2 lemons, one for juice and one sliced

- 1/2 teaspoon ground cinnamon

- dash of salt and pepper

- 1 teaspoon cumin

- 20 grape leaves

- 1 teaspoon dried oregano

- 1/4 cup water

- pinch of allspice

- 3 bay leaves

- 1/4 teaspoon ground ginger

1. Preheat oven to 350 degrees F.

2. In a large skillet, over medium heat, warm the coconut oil. Add the onion and cook until clear. Add the pork, garlic, cinnamon, cumin, oregano, allspice, ginger, coriander and prunes. Cook until the meat is still a little pink.

3. Add the shredded cauliflower and combine with the meat mixture, cooking for 3 minutes. Squeeze the lemon juice over the mixture, season with salt and pepper, and stir. Set the mixture aside until it is cool

enough to handle.

4. Carefully separate the grape leaves and unroll. Spoon a small amount of the meat mixture in the center of the leaf, roll the bottom of the leaf up, then fold the sides over and continue to roll until the end is tucked underneath.

5. Lay the dolmas in a 9×13 baking pan, seam-side down. Lay the lemon slices over the dolmas and squeeze any remaining lemon juice over the pan. Add the water and bay leaves to the pan.

6. Tightly cover with foil. Bake for 30-45 minutes until the leaves turn a dark shade and the water has evaporated. Remove the bay leaves.

7. Serve on a bed of shredded cabbage.

20 DOLMAS

Nutritional Analysis: One serving equals: 88 calories, 4g fat, 25mg sodium, 7g carbohydrate, 2g fiber, and 5g protein

Real Healthy Orange Chicken

Save lots of calories by making this healthy orange chicken rather than take-out.

Here's a recipe that takes all the guilt out of orange-flavored chicken. There's no sugar and no fryer involved. Just skinless, boneless chicken breast, marinated in orange juice, pan seared and then baked. Serve it up with orange-spiked green beans.

Here's what you need for 4 servings:

For the Chicken:

- 2 cups fresh orange juice

- 2 Tablespoons grated orange zest

- 4 skinless, boneless, chicken breasts

For the Green Beans:

- fresh ground pepper

- 1 Tablespoon olive oil

- 10 oz fresh, organic, green beans

- 1/4 cup fresh orange juice

- 1 Tablespoon grated orange zest

For the Orange-Brandy Sauce

- 1 teaspoon olive oil

- dash of salt and pepper

- 2 Tablespoon coconut oil

- 3 shallots, minced

- 2 Tablespoons brandy

- 1 cup fresh orange juice

- 1/2 cup chicken broth

- 1 navel orange, peeled and each segment cut into 3 pieces

- 1 Tablespoon parsley, chopped

- Dash of salt and pepper

Cook the Chicken:
1. Place the orange juice and orange zest in a large

ziplock bag. Season each side of the chicken breasts with salt and pepper. Place the chicken breasts in the ziplock bag, coating each side with juice. Marinate in the refrigerator for 2-3 hours.

2. Preheat the oven to 400 degrees F.

3. Grease a 12-inch, oven-proof skillet with the olive oil. Place over medium-high heat. Add the chicken breasts in a single layer, cooking for 3 minutes. Turn the chicken, season with a sprinkle of salt and pepper. Place the skillet in the oven for 15 minutes, or until a thermometer registers 165 degrees F in the center of the thickest breast.

4. Remove from oven and cover with foil as you make the sauce and cook the beans.

Cook the Green Beans:

1. Wash the beans, snap off and discard the stems. Place in a large ziplock bag with the orange juice and orange zest. Allow to marinate in the refrigerator for 30 minutes.

2. Heat a medium sized skillet over medium heat. Grease with the olive oil. Remove beans from refrigerator, discarding the juice. Add to the skillet and cook, covered for about 5 minutes, stirring occasionally. Remove cover, increase the heat and cook for an additional 3 minutes, until the beans are bright green.

Cook the Sauce:

1. In a medium skillet heat the coconut oil over medium-high heat. Add the minced shallot, cook, stirring often, for 2 minutes. Turn off the heat, add the brandy. Return to the heat and cook, scraping the bottom, until the brandy has almost evaporated, about 30 seconds. Increase the heat to high, add the orange juice. Boil for 5 minutes. Add the chicken broth, boil for 3 minutes.

2. Add in the orange segments and the parsley. Turn off heat. Season with salt and pepper.

To Serve:

1. Cut the chicken on the diagonal into thin slices and arrange over a pile of green beans. Drizzle with the orange-brandy sauce.

4 SERVINGS

Nutritional Analysis: One serving equals: 302 calories, 13g fat, 161mg sodium, 19g carbohydrate, 4g fiber, and 29g protein

Macnut-Crusted Pesto-Stuffed Chicken with Acorn Squash

One look at this chicken dish and you can see that it's something special.

It all started when I found a large bunch of fresh basil and had a hankering for pesto....then entered a bag of macadamia nuts and some free-range chicken tenders. I wasn't really sure where this dish was going to lead, but I'm glad that I took the time to find out. It ended up being one of the most delicious dinners ever.

This recipe has a few extra steps, due to the stuffing and crusting, but it's well worth the effort when you're biting into the tender, flavorful result of your efforts.

Real Healthy Entrees

Here's what you need:

For the Acorn Squash: (If you want to skip the acorn squash, serve on a bed of arugula.)
- 1 acorn squash

- juice from half a lemon (save other half for pesto)

For the Pesto:

- salt and pepper

- 1/2 cup macadamia nuts

- 2 cups fresh basil leaves

- 2 garlic cloves

- 1/3 cup nutritional yeast

For the Chicken:

- Juice from half a lemon

- 1/4 cup olive oil

- dash of sea salt

- 2 lbs boneless skinless chicken tenders

- 1/3 cup Dijon mustard

- 2 Tablespoon olive oil

- 2 Tablespoons pure maple syrup, grade B 1 Tablespoon sweet paprkia

- 1/3 cup macadamia nuts, finely chopped

- 1/8 cup coconut flour

- salt and pepper

1. Preheat oven to 400 degrees F. Lightly grease 2 baking pans with olive oil.

2. For Acorn Squash: Slice the acorn squash in half, scoop out the seeds and using a sharp knife score the inside of the squash flesh. Place in one of the prepared baking pans and drizzle with the lemon juice, and season with salt and pepper. Bake for 50 minutes. Remove from oven and set aside.

3. For Pesto: Place the macadamia nuts, basil leaves, garlic, nutritional yeast, salt and pepper and lemon juice in a food processor. Pulse until well combined while drizzling in the olive oil. Set 1/3 of the pesto aside to serve with the chicken.

4. For Chicken: Rinse the chicken tenders with cold water and pat dry. Place between two sheets of wax paper and lightly pound with the back of a wooden spoon. The idea is to flatten the tenders out so they are wider, yet still intact.

5. Place a tablespoon of pesto in the center of each tender, and spread out until the pesto evenly covers the entire side. Roll the tender up and place, seam side down, in the prepared baking pan, leaving space between each chicken roll.

6. In a small saucepan combine the mustard, olive oil, syrup and paprika over low heat. Mix constantly, and

remove from heat after 3 minutes, when the sauce is uniform. Spread a tablespoon of the mustard sauce over the top of each chicken roll, reserve the leftover sauce.

7. In a small bowl combine the chopped macnuts, coconut flour, salt and pepper. Press a tablespoon of the macadamia nut topping over the top of each chicken roll.

8. Cover the entire pan with foil. Bake for 25 minutes covered. Remove the foil and turn on the high broiler. Broil, watching closely, for 2-5 minutes, until the tops are nicely browned.

9. Scoop the cubed acorn squash out of the shells and place in a skillet over medium heat. Add the reserved mustard sauce, and mix until fully combined. Continue to heat until the squash is fork-tender and the sauce covers each piece.

10. Place a scoop of acorn squash on each plate, then top with slices of chicken roll. Serve with a few dollops of the reserved pesto.

8 SERVINGS

Nutritional Analysis: 328 calories, 17g fat, 614mg sodium, 13g carbohydrate, 3g fiber, and 29g protein

Italian Green Beans & Eggs

Fresh, organic green beans are hard for me to resist when I spot them at the store or farmer's market, but then I find myself wondering how to cook them.

There's the standard green bean salad, but that gets old.

This recipe came about as a combination of whatever-I-had-on-hand and trying to recreate a dish that I'd eaten years ago with the main ingredients of green beans, eggs and tomato.

The tender green beans and onion, soft eggs and tangy-sweet tomato sauce make this side dish both tasty and satisfying. And best of all it's really quick!

Here's what you need:

- 1 TBL olive oil
- 1/2 cup tomato sauce (no sugar added)

- 1 yellow onion, chopped

- 3 omega-3 eggs

- 2 garlic cloves, minced

- 1 teaspoon dried basil

- 3 cups fresh green beans, trimmed and cut

- Salt pepper into 1 inch segments

1. Heat olive oil in large skillet over medium.

2. Add onions and garlic, stirring occasionally until translucent.

3. Add green beans and cover, reduce to low heat. After 8-10 minutes, when beans are bright and tender, remove cover.

4. Add spaghetti sauce. Mix and cook for 3 minutes.

5. In small bowl crack and beat eggs. Add basil, salt and pepper. Add the skillet.

6. Cook, stirring often until eggs are set and sauce is absorbed.

6 Servings

Nutritional Analysis: 85 calories, 4g fat, 142mg sodium, 6g carbohydrate, 3g fiber, and 5g protein

Gluten and Dairy-Free Pizza

This dough recipe calls for yeast, which is gluten-free, that gives the pizza an authentic flavor. If you are able to handle dairy, then sprinkle it with some organic cheese. If not, then enjoy it like I did, with lots of tasty sauce and toppings!

Here's what you need:

- 1 Tablespoon raw honey

- 1 Tablespoon olive oil

- 1 packet (2 tsp) active dry yeast

- 1 teaspoon apple cider vinegar

- 1/4 cup warm, filtered water

- 1/2 cup organic pizza sauce (no sugar added)

- 3/4 cup blanched almond flour

- 3 Tablespoons coconut flour

- 1/2 cup ground sausage

- 1/2 cup arrowroot starch

- 1/2 cup green bell pepper, thinly sliced

- 1/4 teaspoon sea salt

- 1/4 cup red onion, thinly sliced

- 1 omega-3 egg

- 3 Tablespoons sliced black olives

1. Preheat oven to 425 degrees F.

2. Lightly grease a baking sheet with olive oil.

3. In a small bowl combine the honey, yeast and warm water. Mix carefully with a fork. Set aside for 5 minutes, until foamy.

4. In a medium bowl combine the almond flour, coconut flour, arrowroot starch and salt. Work out the lumps with a fork. Add the egg, olive oil and vinegar to the yeast mixture and mix to combine.

5. Add the wet ingredients to the dry ones. Mix well and form a ball of dough. Work the dough for about 30 seconds with your hands, smoothing out any lumps.

6. Place the dough ball in the middle of your prepared pan. Dip your fingers in olive oil, then use them to flatten the dough into your preferred pizza shape (hearts are fun!). Place the dough in preheated oven

for 5-7 minutes.

7. In a small skillet saute the bell pepper and red onion with a drizzle of olive oil for 5 minutes or until tender. Remove from skillet. Add the ground sausage to the skillet and cook until browned, about 5

8. minutes.

9. Top the crust with sauce, sausage, bell pepper, onion and sliced olives. Bake for another 5-7 minutes.

10. Slice and enjoy immediately.

6 SERVINGS

Nutritional Analysis: 244 calories, 12g fat, 339mg sodium, 22g carbohydrate, 4g fiber, and 9g protein

(Bean-less) Chili Loaded Sweet Potato

So why make a bean-less chili? Beans contain phytates which inhibit nutrient absorption and cause inflammation–ever heard the term 'musical fruit'? Beans also contain lectins which can mess with healthy hormonal functions. And to top it off, beans are high in carbohydrates. Beans (also known as legumes) are promoted as a healthy food, because of their fiber, vitamins and minerals, and "high" protein content. In fact, beans aren't a dense protein source, since most contain 2-3 times as many carbs as protein. When compared to vegetables and fruits, beans are lacking in both fiber and micronutrient density.

This dish is easy to put together, just make sure that you afford yourself the 1.5 hours of simmer time.

Here's what you need:

- 3 purple sweet potatoes
- 1 Tablespoon sweet paprika
- 2 Tablespoons olive oil
- pinch of cloves
- 3 cloves garlic, minced
- 1 1/2 Tablespoon unsweetened cocoa
- 3 bell peppers, red, orange and yellow,
- 1 teaspoon ground cinnamon chopped
- 2 teaspoons cumin
- 1 yellow onion, chopped
- 1/2 teaspoon sea salt
- 1.5 pounds ground pork sausage (or your meat of choice)
- 2 (15oz) cans organic tomato sauce ground
- 1 Tablespoon apple cider vinegar
- 1 Tablespoon chilli powder
- 1/2 cup filtered water
- 1/2 teaspoon allspice
- 1 avocado

11. Preheat oven to 400 degrees F. Wash the sweet potatoes and pierce the skin in several places with a knife. Bake for 45 minutes.

12. In a large pot, heat the olive oil over medium. Add garlic, bell peppers and onion. Cook for about 5 minutes, until tender.

13. Add the pork and chili powder and cook until the meat is no longer pink.

14. Add the rest of the spices, tomato sauce, vinegar and water. Bring to a simmer. Reduce heat to low and simmer, uncovered for 1 1/2 hours.

15. To serve: Slice open a piece of sweet potato and top with a big scoop of chili and avocado slices. Season the avocado with lemon juice, cumin, sweet paprika and sea salt.

   * For a meal lower in carbs, serve your chili over scrambled eggs instead of sweet potato

8 SERVINGS

Nutritional Analysis: 272 calories, 11g fat, 532mg sodium, 24g carbohydrate, 7g fiber, and 22g protein

Real Healthy Broccoli and Beef

This recipe for Real Healthy Broccoli and Beef has all the attributes of the perfect weeknight dinner...

1. It's very quick to throw together.

2. It's bursting with protein and fiber.

3. It's low in carbs.

4. It has aaaaaaaaaaaamazing flavor!

5. It doesn't contain any gluten, soy, sugar or MSG.

In my book this dinner recipe gets a perfect 10!

Real Healthy Entrees

Here's what you need:

- 2/3 cup coconut aminos
- 2 Tablespoon Olive oil, divided
- 1 1/2 Tablespoons fresh ginger, minced
- 1 bunch green onions, chopped
- 4 garlic cloves, minced
- 4 cups organic broccoli, cut into small pieces
- 1/2 cup filtered water
- 1/3 cup pure maple syrup, grade b
- 1.5 lbs grassfed flank, skirt or minute steak, cut into very thin strips
- 3 Tablespoons arrowroot starch

1. In a medium bowl combine the coconut aminos, ginger, garlic, water, syrup and arrowroot. Set aside.

2. Heat 1 tablespoon of the olive oil, on high, in a large skillet or wok. Add the green onions and broccoli, saute for 5 minutes. Remove from skillet.

3. Heat the remaining 1 tablespoon of olive oil and stir-fry the steak until almost done, about 4 minutes.

4. Return the veggies to the skillet and add the sauce. Heat until the sauce boils and thickens, about 3 minutes.

5. Serve over Stir Fried Cauliflower rice.

6 SERVINGS

Nutritional Analysis: 371 calories, 14g fat, 684mg sodium, 15g carbohy-drate, 2g fiber, and 34g protein

(Gluten-Free & Sugar-Free) Awesome Crispy Orange Chicken

I used to LOVE getting crispy orange chicken from our old favorite Chinese take-out restaurant, and sometimes would even get frozen crispy orange chicken from the store to cook up for a quick dinner. While those traditional orange chicken dishes tasted great they were filled with gluten, sugar, soy and unhealthy fats.

So I created this recipe for crispy orange chicken with zero gluten, sugar or soy. It is sweetened with fruit-only orange juice concentrate and zero-calorie Stevia.

This dish is really quick to throw together for a weeknight dinner, and tastes so good you won't believe it's healthy. As a bonus you won't get that big bellyache like with the take-out version.

Here's what you need:

- 1/2 cup orange juice concentrate (no sugar
- 1 tablespoon coconut oil added)
- 2.5 lbs boneless skinless chicken thigh, cut into bite sized pieces
- 3 Tablespoons coconut aminos
- 1 Tablespoon olive oil
- Dash salt and pepper
- Zest from one orange
- Dash granulated onion
- 3 cloves garlic, minced
- 1 tablespoon sesame seeds
- Dash red pepper flakes
- 3 green onions, chopped
- 2 packets Stevia

1. Combine the orange juice concentrate, coconut aminos, olive oil, orange zest, red pepper flakes and Stevia in a small bowl. Mix well and set aside.

2. In a large skillet, heat the coconut oil on medium-high.

3. Generously season the chicken pieces with salt, pepper and granulated onion. Add chicken to hot

skillet and brown on all sides.

4. When chicken is almost fully cooked, add the orange sauce, stirring to coat all of the chicken. Cook, uncovered, simmering the sauce until thickened and fully sticking to the chicken.

5. Garnish with sesame seeds and freshly chopped green onion.

6 Servings

Nutritional Analysis: One Serving Equals, 282 calories, 12g fat, 505mg sodium, 12g carbs, 1g fiber, 35g protein

Real Healthy Meatloaf

Who doesn't have fond memories of meatloaf dinners?

Of course that traditional meatloaf had gluten in it and corn syrup-filled ketchup slathered on top. Not OK for our evolved, healthy diet.

This recipe uses healthy, grassfed beef and takes out the gluten and corn syrup. The hard boiled egg surprise in the middle is a fun way to pack in some more protein.

Here's what you need:

- 1/2 cup unsweetened coconut milk

- 1 1/2 lbs grassfed ground beef

- 1 egg, beaten

- 1 cup mushrooms, chopped

- Dash of salt and pepper

- 1 yellow onion, chopped

- 1 Tablespoon balsamic vinegar glaze

- 4 hard boiled eggs, peeled

- 1 cup almond meal

For Glaze:

- 1/2 cup homemade ketchup

- 2 Tablespoons balsamic vinegar glaze

1. Preheat oven to 350 degrees F.

2. In a large mixing bowl combine the coconut milk, egg, salt and pepper, balsamic glaze, and almond meal.

3. Add the ground beef, mushrooms, and onion. Press half of the mixture in a loaf pan. Line up the 4 hard boiled eggs (see picture) and then press the remaining beef mixture on top. Smooth out the top. Bake for an hour.

4. While the meatloaf bakes, mix the ketchup and balsamic glaze. After an hour of baking, remove the meatloaf from oven, pour the glaze over the top and smooth out. Return to oven for 10 minutes.

5. Serve with cauliflower rice. \

6 SERVINGS

Nutritional Analysis: One serving equals: 397 calories, 23g fat, 143mg sodium, 11g carbohydrate, 3g fiber, and 32g protein

Blackberry Chicken Tenders on Asparagus

This fast, tasty dinner recipe centers around protein and veggies. Blackberries add a unique and unexpected flavor.

Here's what you need:

For the Chicken:

- 1.5 pounds organic, skinless, boneless
- 1 Tablespoon olive oil
- chicken tenders
- 1/8 cup yellow onion, minced

- 1 cup organic blackberries

- 4 garlic cloves, minced

- 1/4 cup coconut aminos

- 1 packet Stevia

- 1/4 cup plum vinegar

6. Rinse the chicken tenders and pat dry. Place in a large ziplock bag.

7. Combine the rest of the ingredients in a high speed blender until smooth.

8. *optional* Strain the seeds from marinade (If you don't mind the crunch, then leave the seeds in!)

9. Pour the marinade into the bag of chicken, seal and place in the refrigerator for 4 to 6 hours.

10. Preheat oven to 375 degrees F. Place the marinated chicken in a baking pan and bake for 30 minutes.

11. Remove from oven, drain off excess marinade, then place under high broil for 4 minutes, watching closely.

4 SERVINGS

Nutritional Analysis: One serving equals: 237 calories, 4g fat, 655mg sodium, 11g carbohydrate, 3g fiber, and 35g protein

For the Blackberry Sauce:

- 1 TBL coconut oil

- 1 packet Stevia

- 1 cup organic blackberries

- 1 Tbl plum vinegar

1. In a skillet over medium low heat, combine all of the ingredients and bring to a simmer.

2. Simmer, stirring often, until the blackberries become bright and the sauce reaches desired consistency.

3. If you wish to thicken the sauce more, add 1/2 teaspoon of arrowroot powder.

4. *optional* Strain the seeds from the sauce (If you don't mind the crunch, then leave the seeds in!)

5. Serve over the cooked chicken.

SAUCE: 4 SERVINGS

Nutritional Analysis: One serving equals: 50 calories, 3g fat, 0mg sodium, 4g carbohydrate, 2g fiber, and 1g protein

For the Asparagus:

- 1 bunch skinny asparagus, ends trimmed and

- Dash of Salt and pepper cut into 1-inch pieces

- 2 cloves garlic, minced

- 1 Tablespoon Olive oil

- 1 Tablespoon lemon juice

1. Preheat oven to 375 degrees F. Lightly grease a baking sheet with olive oil.

2. In a bowl combine the asparagus, oil, salt, pepper, garlic and lemon juice. Spread over prepared pan.

3. Bake for 17 minutes, or until tender and bright green.

4 SERVINGS

Nutritional Analysis: One serving equals: 55 calories, 3g fat, 66mg sodium, 5g carbohydrate, 2g fiber, and 2g protein

44

Whole Roasted Chicken and Veggies

One of the most satisfying things to make for dinner is a whole roasted organic chicken, flanked with organic, herb-coated veggies. It looks super impressive without being difficult at all to make. And best of all it only takes very little actual prep time.

This is the recipe that I use for my Sunday roasted chicken. Serve with a fresh loaf of almond bread. Divine!

Here's what you need:

- 3 bulbs garlic

- 4 large organic carrots, cut into 1 inch pieces

- 1/4 cup olive oil

- 3 organic zucchini, cut into 1 inch half-moons

- salt and pepper

- 4 Tablespoons coconut oil, gently melted

- 1 cup pearl onions, ends trimmed

- 1 Tablespoon each minced, fresh rosemary, oregano, tarragon

- 1 cup Brussels sprouts, halved

- 1 hormone-free, organic chicken

- 1 teaspoon minced garlic

- 2 cups chicken broth

- zest and juice from one lemon

- 1 Tablespoon coconut flour

1. Preheat the oven to 400 degrees F.

2. Cut off the tips of each section of the garlic bulbs. Place the blubs in a small glass pan. Brush the tops with the olive oil and sprinkle with salt and pepper. Cover the pan with aluminum foil and set aside.

3. In a small bowl combine the melted coconut oil, fresh herbs, minced garlic, lemon zest and lemon juice. Set 1/3 of the mixture aside for the veggies.

4. In a large bowl combine the carrots, zucchini, pearl onions and Brussels sprouts with 1/3 of the herb mixture. Season with salt and pepper. Set aside.

5. Rinse your chicken and pat dry. Carefully slide your hand between the skin and the breast and liberally

rub some of the herb mixture. Rub the rest of the herb mixture over the top of the chicken. Season the chicken with salt and pepper and tie the legs together with kitchen string. Place the chicken on a large roasting pan, and surround it with the veggies.

6. Roast the chicken and veggies for 30 minutes. Reduce the oven temperature to 350 degrees F, pour 1/2 cup of chicken broth over the chicken and veggies, and place the garlic pan in the oven off to the side.

7. For the next 90 minutes, pour 1/2 cup of broth over the chicken and veggies every 30 minutes as it cooks at 350 degrees F.

8. To see if the chicken is done, poke the tip of a sharp knife between the leg and body and see that the juices run clear. Transfer the chicken and veggies to a large platter. Add a couple of the roasted garlic bulbs to the chicken platter, reserving one for the gravy.

9. To make gravy: Pour all of the roasting pan juices into a skillet and bring to a simmer. Remove the garlic cloves from one of the roasted blubs and smash with a fork. Add garlic to skillet. Mix in the tablespoon of coconut flour, and whisk the gravy as it simmers. Cook for 10 minutes, or until desired thickness. Season with salt and pepper.

5 SERVINGS

Nutritional Analysis: One serving equals: 251 calories, 14g fat, 113mg sodium, 19g carbohydrate, 7g fiber, and 17g protein

Vegetable Soup with Savory Pesto

If you are a fan of minestrone soup, but don't want the carbs of beans and noodles, then you'll love this allvegetable alternative. The strands of cabbage mimic those of noodles and the pesto adds amazing flavor.

Here's what you need for 10 servings:

For the Soup:

- 1 Tablespoon olive oil
- 1 cup organic cauliflower pieces
- 1 large organic yellow onion, chopped
- 3 Tablespoons fresh Rosemary, minced
- 1 organic red bell pepper, chopped

- 3 Tablespoon fresh Italian parsley, minced

- 2 large organic carrots, chopped

- 2 bay leaves

- 4 garlic cloves, minced

- 8 cups chicken broth

- 1 small organic green cabbage, thinly sliced

For the Pesto:

- 4 garlic cloves

- juice from half a lemon

- 2 cups basil leaves

- 1/2 cup nutritional yeast

- 1/2 cup walnuts

- 1 cup olive oil

1. In a large soup pot, over medium heat, warm the olive oil. Add onion, bell pepper, carrots, and garlic. Cook until the vegetables are tender.

2. Add the cabbage, cauliflower pieces, rosemary, parsley and bay leaves. After 5 minutes add the chicken stock. Allow to simmer, covered for 20 minutes then season with salt and pepper.

3. For the Pesto: In a food processor, combine the garlic, basil, walnuts, lemon juice and nutritional yeast. Pulse until all ingredients are mixed in. With the blade

spinning, slowly pour in the olive oil. Continue to blend until the mixture is smooth.

4. Fill each soup bowl with the soup and top with a generous spoonful of the pesto.

ONE SERVING EQUALS: 170 CALORIES, 11G FAT, 182MG SODIUM, 10G CARBOHYDRATE, 4G FIBER, AND 5G PROTEIN

Cold Day Chicken Soup

A time-tested way of showing love is to share homemade soup.

This Cold Day Chicken Soup is extra special as it doesn't contain any high-carb ingredients like noodles or potatoes, like most do.

Enjoy and allow this simple, nourishing meal warm you from the inside out.

Here's what you need for 8 servings:

- 1 Tablespoon coconut oil

- 3 cups diced roasted chicken

- 1 medium organic yellow onion, chopped

- 1 bay leaf

- 3 carrots, grated

- 1 organic apple, chopped

- 2 celery stalks, finely chopped

- dash of salt and pepper

- 1 Tablespoon curry powder

- 1/2 teaspoon dried thyme

- 2 garlic cloves, crushed

- zest from 1 lemon

- 2 quarts chicken broth

- 2 cups unsweetened coconut milk

1. In a large pot, over medium heat, melt the coconut oil and add the onion, carrots and celery. After 5 minutes add the garlic and curry powder.

2. After a couple minutes add the chicken broth, chicken, bay leave, apple, pepper, thyme, and lemon zest.

3. Stir well. Bring to a simmer and cook for 40 minutes.

4. Stir in the coconut milk, and some salt if desired, remove the bay leaf and serve.

8 SERVINGS

Nutritional Analysis: One serving equals: 166 calories, 5g fat, 175mg sodium, 9g carbohydrate, 2g fiber, and 19g protein

Teriyaki Chicken Plate

A marinade can make or break the flavor of your meal.

This marinade uses Zevia lemon lime soda, which is sweetened with stevia, making it all natural and calorie free. This adds sweetness to the chicken without cane sugar. The intensity of the flavor, when marinated overnight, is amazing.

I like to serve this over a big bed of baby arugula and a scoop of cooked quinoa.

Here's what you need for 4 servings:

- 1 can naturally sweetened, zero calorie

- 1 Tablespoon coconut crystals (or 1 lemon lime soda (Zevia brand) teaspoon agave nectar or 1 packet Stevia)

- ½ cup soy sauce

- 2 pounds boneless, skinless chicken thighs

- ¾ cup brown rice vinegar

- 2 teaspoons coconut oil

- 1 medium yellow onion – half minced and half thinly sliced

- 1 bunch asparagus, trimmed and cut into 1-inch segments

- 4 cloves garlic, smashed

- 2 Tablespoons chopped cilantro

- 1 Tablespoon fresh ginger, grated optional

*baby arugula and cooked quinoa

1. Combine the soda, soy sauce, vinegar, minced onion, garlic, ginger and coconut crystals in a bowl. Add the chicken and turn to coat. Place in refrigerator overnight.

2. Remove chicken from marinade and pat dry. Reserve 1 cup of marinade.

3. Heat one teaspoon of coconut oil in a large skillet. Add the chicken and heat on medium high, turning once, for 8-10 minutes, until browned and cooked through. Transfer to a plate.

4. Wipe out the skillet. Heat remaining 1 teaspoon of coconut oil. Add the sliced onion and asparagus.

Cook for 5 minutes, until browned. Add the reserved marinade and boil until slightly reduced. Add the cilantro.

5. Serve over a bed of baby arugula and cooked quinoa.

4 Servings

One serving equals: 289 calories, 13g fat, 963mg sodium, 4.8g carbohydrate, 3g fiber, and 29g protein

Turkey Kebabs with Mint Yogurt Dip

This Mediterranean dinner is easy to put together and tastes amazing.

The turkey kebabs are high in protein, and the rest of the plate is filled with savory, fiber-filled veggies. It's very satisfying without the waist-expanding carbs that most dinners are filled with.

Here's what you need for the Turkey Kebabs:

- 1 1/2 pounds turkey breast, de-boned,

- 1 teaspoon cumin trimmed of skin and cut into thin strips

- 1 teaspoon sweet paprika

- 2 garlic cloves, minced

- 1/2 teaspoon cinnamon

- 1 teaspoon olive oil

- dash of salt (optional)

- 2 eggs

- 2 Tablespoons fresh parsley, finely chopped

- 1/4 cup almond meal (more if needed)

- 1 Tablespoon fresh mint, finely chopped

1. In a food processor, blend the turkey strips until ground. Add the remaining ingredients and pulse until well blended.

2. Pre-heat your grill or grill pan.

3. Lightly grease your hands, then press the meat into the wooden skewers until it covers about 3-4 inches in an elongated meatball shape. If the meat is not sticking then add some more almond meal.

4. Grill for about 8 minutes per side.

4 SERVINGS

Nutritional Analysis: One serving equals: 254 calories, 8g fat, 156mg sodium, 2g carbohydrate, 1g fiber, and 47g protein

For the Mint Yogurt Dip:

- 1 cup plain Greek yogurt, full fat

- 1 garlic clove, minced

- 2 Tablespoons fresh mint, minced 1 Tablespoon

freshly squeezed lemon juice

- salt (optional)

1. In a bowl combine all of the ingredients. Mix well and serve chilled.

4 Servings

One serving equals: 69 calories, 5g fat, 35mg sodium, 3g carbohydrate, .1g fiber, and 2.3g protein

Chicken Sausage, Cauliflower and Kale Casserole

The only way that I used to eat cauliflower was slathered in real mayonnaise and then smothered with cheese. Not exactly healthy. What I love about this casserole is that the ricotta cheese gives you the creamy cauliflower experience, while also sneaking in kale — which is high in calcium and has loads of vitamins — and some chicken sausage for protein.

This nutritional jackpot takes home cooked comfort food to a real healthy place.

Here's what you need for 6 servings:

- 1 teaspoon olive oil

- 4 links nitrate-free, chicken sausage, sliced

- 1 yellow onion, diced into half moons

- 2 garlic cloves, minced

- 1 head cauliflower, cut into small florets

- 3 cups kale, chopped

- 1/2 cup chicken broth

- dash of salt and pepper

- 1 teaspoon lemon juice

- Pinch of each, dried: thyme, rosemary, tarragon, and parsley

- 1 cup fat free ricotta cheese

- 1/2 cup Parmesan cheese, shredded and divided

Preheat oven to 425 degrees F. Lightly grease a casserole dish with olive oil. Place a large pot of water to boil with a pinch of salt.

1. In a large skillet over medium heat, saute the olive oil, onion, garlic, salt and pepper, dried herbs and chicken sausage. Mix well, then add kale. Cover for about 3 minutes, until kale gets bright green and wilted, then remove cover. Saute for an additional 3 minutes until everything is tender. Set aside.

2. Place the cauliflower florets in the pot of boiling water. Boil for 5 minutes, then remove from heat, drain, and return cauliflower to pot.

3. Add the kale mixture to the pot as well as the chicken broth, lemon juice, ricotta cheese and half of the Parmesan cheese. Mix will over medium heat until all

has been incorporated.

4. Transfer to prepared casserole dish. Top with remaining Parmesan cheese. Cover with foil and bake for 15 minutes. Remove foil and bake for an additional 5 minutes.

5. Remove from oven and serve.

6 SERVINGS

One serving equals: 238 calories, 10g fat, 584mg sodium, 14g carbohydrate, 4g fiber, and 18g protein

About Advantage Personal Training LLC.

We developed this book to show you that you can eat healthily and still enjoy food. You don't have to be on starvation diets or eating things that do not taste good.

At Advantage Personal Training you will meet with a professional coach and you will be working with our nationally acclaimed caring and motivating transformation team every step of the way... and you'll have an absolute blast doing it!

GETTING STARTED IS EASY

Just call us in Mystic, CT at 860-245-0388 or Niantic, CT at **860-691-1616**

or

email us at **Info@AdvantagePersonalTraining.com** and we will set you up for a complimentary consultation to see if Advantage is the perfect place for you to reach your health, fitness, and fat loss goals.

.

.

Made in USA - Kendallville, IN
65813_9781736594131
01.20.2022 1358